Spartacus

The story of the rebellious Thracian gladiator

Spartacus

The story of the rebellious Thracian gladiator

TONY BRADMAN
with Tom Bradman

A & C Black • London

First published 2010 by
A & C Black Publishers Ltd
36 Soho Square, London, W1D 3QY

www.acblack.com

ISBN 978-1-4081-1335-6

A CIP catalogue for this book is available from the British Library.

Printed and bound in Great Britain
by CPI Cox & Wyman, Reading RG1 8EX.

1
The Power of Rome

Summer 74BC

The boy stood with the warriors of his tribe, watching the Romans march up the hill towards them. Sunlight glittered off the Roman helmets and shields and weapons, and the tramping of Roman feet made the ground shake.

The ground of Thrace, the boy thought. His homeland, the only place he had ever known.

'Steady, lads,' said the chief, the boy's father. 'Wait till I give the word.'

Around the boy were his brothers, and beyond them in the line of warriors he could see his uncles and cousins and friends and neighbours, all holding shields and swords or spears. They were young and old and every age in between, but each face was grim, whether it was smooth or bearded. Behind them in the valleys were their homes, and the wives and families they were protecting.

The invaders had come in the spring, and the tribe had fought them. So the Romans had burnt villages and slaughtered men, women and children, the red crests of their helmets like a tide of fire and blood.

Of course, raiders often came to kill and burn – the Thracian tribes fought each other regularly. But the Romans were different – they wanted to take away the people's freedom and rule them as part of their empire.

The boy's tribe had gathered to make a final stand, to drive the Romans back over the mountains and sea – or die trying.

'They've stopped!' somebody hissed.

The boy looked down the hillside and saw it was true. The Romans had halted and locked their shields, making a wall of wood and iron, the tips of their spears pointing up above. Commands were being shouted behind it in the Latin tongue, which sounded strange to the boy's ears.

'Hear me, men of Thrace,' the chief yelled suddenly, his voice echoing off the surrounding hills. 'I have been told what it means to be a slave of the Romans. To be bought and sold like animals. To be treated as if you were a beast of burden. That is why I fight them – to keep my life my own, and that is why I swore to keep my people free. Are you with me in this? Shall we turn them back here, together, and show them just what Thracian warriors are made of?'

The warriors clashed their weapons on their shields and roared their approval, their defiance of Rome and its soldiers and its empire.

The chief nodded, a smile on his face. Then he yelled, 'With me, lads … *NOW!*' and charged forward, his sword held high, the bright sunlight flashing off his helmet.

His warriors ran after him, screaming their war cries, their feet pounding on the dry ground.

The boy charged, too, whooping and yelling like all the rest.

The Romans threw their spears and many of the warriors fell, their war cries changing to screams of fear and pain. Those still on their feet kept running, crashing at last into the Roman shields, and the boy found himself in a struggling mass of bodies, men pushing and shoving, blades slashing and hacking and stabbing.

But the Roman shield wall held, and before long it started to move again, forcing the warriors backwards, men dying with every step. The boy gave ground slowly, banging his sword into the Roman shields until he tripped on a body and fell. The Romans trampled over him with their iron-shod sandals.

'Spartacus!' he heard somebody scream, for that was his name, and he turned just in time to see his father trying to hack a way through to him, cutting down legionaries with his long sword. But the Thracian chief's path also led him towards the Roman general sitting on his horse, calmly giving orders, directing his men.

The boy's father never had a chance. The general's bodyguards quickly surrounded him in a ring of steel. Blades flashed and the chief fell, blood pouring from a dozen wounds, any one of which would have been enough to kill him.

Then the edge of a Roman shield slammed into

the boy's head, and the shouting and the clanging of weapons faded into silence and darkness…

When Spartacus woke, he was lying on his side and his hands were tied behind him with rough twine. He struggled into a sitting position and saw that he was in a group of twenty or so warriors of his tribe, the only survivors of the battle, none of whom were related to him. Their hands were tied as well, and Roman soldiers stood guard over them. More Roman soldiers were stacking captured swords and spears in heaps, or dragging the bodies of the dead over to a huge fire.

Spartacus closed his eyes, hoping the nightmare would go away… But it didn't. Then he heard a couple of the warriors whispering to each other.

'I just wish they'd get a move on if they're going to kill us,' hissed one.

'Huh, no such luck,' grunted the second man. 'They have something far worse in mind. I bet we're all going to Rome … to be sold as slaves.'

The voices whispered on, but Spartacus had stopped listening. He said a silent prayer to the

LIVESinACTION

Gods of his tribe, and made a vow. The Romans might think they could force him to live as a slave, but whatever happened, wherever they took him and whatever they made him do, he promised himself something – he would die a free man...

2
A World of Slaves

Late summer 74BC

The journey from Thrace was long and hard. Spartacus and the other captives were chained together and marched over the mountains, the Romans whipping anyone who showed defiance, then they were loaded onto a big ship with hundreds of prisoners. Dozens died on the voyage, but the Romans didn't seem to care.

'Plenty more where this one came from!' laughed a Roman soldier as he helped to throw the limp, dead body of a captive over the side.

'I think this one fancies a swim,' said another legionary, kicking Spartacus. 'If he's lucky, the pirates will fish him out and sell him back to us!'

Spartacus said nothing and looked away. He had soon realised he couldn't escape, and had decided to wait until he had a better chance. Meanwhile, he kept his head down and avoided getting into any trouble. All the same, he found it hard to stomach the way the Romans treated their captives. Were they really so rich in slaves that it didn't matter how many died on voyages like this?

That question was answered when the ship arrived and the captives were marched into the great city. Spartacus had never seen anything like it. The huts in his village had been made of wood and thatch, but the streets of Rome were lined with gigantic buildings made of red bricks, and there were white temples with tall columns. Compared to these places, even his father's great hall, the building that held everyone in the village on feast days, would have looked tiny. But there was barely time to take it all in before the captives came to a large open space, and were shoved into enormous cages packed with chained-up people.

There were men and women and children, and most of them spoke tongues Spartacus couldn't understand. And more kept coming. Every so often, the cage doors would be opened, and another group of terrified captives would be shoved inside. Now Spartacus could see what the Roman soldier on the ship had meant. There *were* plenty more slaves where the dead man had come from. It seemed the Romans were determined to make everyone in the world their slaves...

People didn't stay in the cages long. The guards constantly took groups of captives out, and after a while it was the turn of the Thracians. The cage doors were opened, and men with whips and spears pushed and shoved them across the open space to a kind of wooden platform surrounded by a large, noisy crowd.

'I don't like the look of this,' said one of the Thracians. 'What's going on?'

'Isn't it obvious?' muttered the man beside him. 'We're being sold off.'

Spartacus realised his fellow captive was right. The men in the crowd were shouting and pointing. He couldn't understand what they were saying, but he could see that a man standing with the guards at the side of the platform was in charge. This man – the overseer – shouted back, and soon most of the Thracians were being unchained and dragged away by the guards of their new owners.

After a while, a thin, mean-looking man pushed his way through the crowd and came to stand right in front of Spartacus. This man yelled something at the overseer, who shrugged. Then the man nodded to the big guard beside him, and the two of them climbed onto the platform. Soon the guard was poking and prodding the captive, roughly squeezing his arm muscles. It made Spartacus feel like a horse being sold at a country fair, and hot anger boiled inside him.

Eventually, the guard forced his fingers into the young Thracian's mouth and peered at his teeth. Something inside Spartacus snapped and he pulled back, swinging a fist at the man's face. But the guard casually blocked the blow and brought his knee up into the boy's groin. Spartacus fell to the ground, pain shooting through his stomach, and the guard laughed, shaking his head. The mean-looking man smiled, too, and spoke to the guard, gesturing at the boy.

'My master, the noble Lentulus Batiatus thinks you have spirit, and so do I,' said the guard. 'He

wants to know if you have ever done any fighting.'
He was speaking Thracian, but with a thick accent.

The boy looked at the guard, surprised. 'Why
does he want to know that?' he asked, standing
up unsteadily. 'And how is it that you speak my
tongue? You're not Thracian, are you?'

'No, I am Crixus the German,' said the guard.
'But I know many tongues – Latin, Greek, Gaulish
– and my master uses me to speak for him. If I
were you, I would tell him that you've done lots of
fighting, even if you haven't.'

'But why would someone want a slave who can
fight?' said Spartacus.

'Because he needs men to fight for him in the
arena,' said Crixus. 'And believe me, it's much better
than being worked to death in the hot sun on
a farm.'

Spartacus stared at Crixus – then at his new
master. Lentulus Batiatus grinned. And for the first
time since the battle, Spartacus almost smiled,
too. Who knew what might happen if the Romans
put a sword in his hand?

3

Gladiator School

Late summer 74BC to summer 73BC

Lentulus Batiatus bought another half-dozen Thracian men, and the next day had them loaded into an open wagon drawn by two big oxen. The slaves were chained together, and then Crixus climbed into the wagon, too, along with several hard-faced guards, all of them armed with whips and clubs. The noble rode his horse beside the wagon, chatting to the driver.

'Cheer up, boy,' said Crixus. 'Trust me, things could be a lot worse. At least you'll get plenty of good food and wine now you're going to be a gladiator.'

'But who will I fight?' asked Spartacus. 'And

what is a gladiator?'

'You'll find out soon enough,' snorted Crixus. 'Just enjoy the ride.'

They left Rome by its southern gate, and travelled for the next two days down the Appian Way, a long road that passed through mile after mile of rich farmland. Spartacus saw huge gangs of slaves working in the fields, the hot Italian sun beating down on them. Eventually the wagon arrived at its destination – a cluster of buildings at the edge of a town. A large structure stood in the middle, a round building with several big doors, but no roof of any kind.

'Welcome to the Gladiator School of our noble master Lentulus Batiatus, the finest in Capua,' said Crixus, jumping off the wagon. 'Step this way, lads…'

Spartacus climbed down from the wagon and followed the big German.

The boy immediately noticed that the buildings were surrounded by a tall wooden fence with more guards outside it – and these men were proper Roman soldiers. For a brief moment his heart sank, and he began to fear he would never manage to escape. Then he gritted his teeth and forced himself to stay calm. He would watch and wait, and he would find a way to get out…

Crixus led the slaves into a central courtyard and arranged them in a ragged line. A crowd of hard-looking men stared from within a long iron cage on the far side. They must be gladiators, thought Spartacus, whatever that meant. He held his head high, reminding himself that he was the son of a great warrior chief. Even so, his stomach was churning with apprehension. At last, Crixus chose a short wooden sword from a rack full of them, and stood before the new arrivals.

'All right, this is what you've been waiting for, the chance to get back at your oppressors,' Crixus said, looking deep into the eyes of each slave. 'Any man here who thinks he can beat me in a fight should take a step forward now.'

Spartacus didn't hesitate, and Crixus smiled, throwing the wooden sword to him. The boy caught it and charged, taking a wild swing at the big German, all his fury and frustration channelled into the blow. He missed, and a fist like a rock slammed into his ear. Spartacus staggered, shaking his head to clear it, then turned to face Crixus again. But Crixus rammed his fist into the boy's middle, forcing the air out of his lungs and knocking him to the ground. Spartacus could hear the others sniggering, and tried to get up, although he could barely breathe.

Crixus put a sandalled foot on his chest and gently pushed him back. 'Stay down, boy,' the big German whispered, and then he turned to face the line of slaves. 'I don't know why you think it's funny. Only the youngest of you dared fight me! But soon you will all fight in the arena beyond that wall. You'll fight for your life against trained killers, and you'll be laughed at, booed and jeered! The audience pays to see men die, to see their blood spilled, and you'll give them what they want, one way or another. Remember now, from this moment on, you are here to fight and die for the pleasure of the Romans.'

No one was laughing any more.

Their training began at dawn the next morning. Crixus was hard on Spartacus, pitting him regularly against Oenomaus, a huge Gaul. Oenomaus was twice the size of the young Thracian and didn't hold back in a fight. But Spartacus soon learned the benefits of being light on his feet, using his natural agility to counter brute strength and aggression. When they sparred, Oenomaus was all business. After training, however, he was one of the most friendly, his booming laugh filling the barracks.

Crixus was always there, making Spartacus train even harder, giving him tips and advice – where to strike, how to parry a blow and turn defence into attack. Whenever Spartacus was wounded, Crixus had a salve or ointment to help ease the pain and make him get better.

The days and months went by, and Spartacus grew bigger and stronger. The training helped, and Crixus had been telling the truth – the gladiators *were* given plenty of good food and wine, and they were well looked after, with baths and massages to ease their aching limbs. But they were still locked in at night.

Lentulus Batiatus waited nearly a full year before he put Spartacus in for his first contest. It was a small event, a mere twenty pairs of men fighting while the crowd cheered and booed, and ate and drank the dried fruit and wine Lentulus sold them.

Spartacus had been trained to fight as a 'Samnite', which meant he wore a particular type of gladiator outfit comprised of a high-crested helmet and light upper-body armour, and he carried a small round shield and a curved sword.

Crixus had told Spartacus he was a natural, and the fight went well. His opponent was equipped as a 'Retiarius' – he held a net and trident; a long, three-pronged spear.

The man was taller and older than Spartacus, and should have easily caught the inexperienced boy with his net. But Spartacus was skilful and very quick on his feet. At last the Retiarius threw the net and missed, and Spartacus charged, knocking the man to the ground. Spartacus stood over him, his sword point on the man's chest. One thrust and the man's blood would stain the sand beneath him like that of the others who had already been killed.

21

The crowd bayed, jabbing their thumbs downwards in the traditional gesture that meant they wanted the Retiarius finished off. Spartacus looked round at the faces made ugly by their lust for blood. Then he turned to his opponent, whose blue eyes were locked on his. They both knew that if Spartacus spared him, the crowd would only demand the young Thracian's death instead. The Retiarius nodded, and Spartacus nodded back. He killed the man, and walked away.

Later, in the bath house where the survivors cleaned off the blood and sweat and had their wounds tended, Crixus came and sat beside a brooding Spartacus.

'You did well,' said the German, putting his arm round the boy's shoulders. They were friends now, comrades of the arena. 'The crowd loves a winner.'

'Perhaps one day I'll show them what I can really do…' said Spartacus.

He had devised a plan at last, and the time would soon come to reveal it.

4

The Keys to Freedom

Summer 73BC

A few days later, Spartacus gathered some of the gladiators in a dark corner of the bath house to talk to them. Crixus and Oenomaus were there, as well as a dozen more. They sat in a semi-circle round the young Thracian, curious.

'I have a question to ask you all,' Spartacus said quietly. He was speaking the rough slave Latin he had learned, the only tongue most slaves had in common. 'I will be leaving this evil place soon. Who will come with me when I escape?'

'Don't talk daft, Spartacus,' said Crixus with a deep sigh. 'The guards will catch you as soon as you climb over the fence. Then you'll be punished.'

'Well, if that happens, so be it,' murmured Spartacus, shrugging. 'They can whip me, and brand me with hot irons, or they can kill me. If I stay here I'm going to die in the arena, and so will every man in this room – and that includes you, Crixus. Trying to escape is the only chance we have of staying alive.'

'He does have a point, Crixus,' growled Oenomaus, scratching his beard. 'You and I have been gladiators too long. Our luck could run out any day soon.'

'Do you really want to die to give the Romans pleasure?' said Spartacus. 'I know I don't. My mind is made up. I won't kill anyone for them again, either,' he added.

Crixus stared at his young friend silently for a moment, then raised a bushy eyebrow. 'Fair enough,' said the German. 'But you've still got to convince me that we *can* make it out of here. I've seen men try and fail, although something tells me the only reason you're talking about this is because you've got a sure-fire plan.'

'You're not half as stupid as you look, Crixus,' said Spartacus, smiling at the big German. 'As a matter of fact I *do* have a plan. We need to get a bunch of keys from one of the overseers, and I think I know how. Then, once we're out of the school, we head for the hills and lie low for a couple of weeks, or till things quieten down. After that we make for the nearest coast, find a ship –'

'Simple as that, eh?' said Crixus. He looked at Oenomaus, who nodded. 'Well, why not? Count me in,' he said. 'What about the rest of you?'

There was general agreement among the men, but that wasn't enough for Spartacus. He made them stand in a circle, their arms around each other.

'Now, swear after me!' he said. 'Brothers we are, and brothers we stay!'

They did as they were told, and Spartacus could feel a strange power flowing between them. From this moment on, there was no going back, no giving in.

The next afternoon, Spartacus trained with Oenomaus again. They fought hard, just as they always did, and after a short while, Oenomaus swung his wooden sword at the young Thracian's head. Spartacus failed to parry it and fell to the ground as if he'd been knocked out, Oenomaus calling for help. Such things often happened in training, and Lentulus Batiatus had given strict orders that his costly gladiators were to be looked after. So Spartacus soon felt himself being carried off.

He opened his eyes as an overseer and a guard took him into a small room behind the bath house. They dumped him on a table and turned away to get the dressing ready for his bleeding head. Without a sound, he rose from the table and found the club Crixus had left beneath it earlier. He raised the club and brought it down on the guard's skull with all his strength. The guard fell to the floor, and the young Thracian quickly turned to the overseer. The club whistled through the air and made a dent the size of a man's fist in the overseer's temple, killing him instantly. Spartacus took the man's keys and, as the sun was setting, he was able to sneak through the shadows back to the barracks without being seen.

'Thank the gods!' said Oenomaus with a

huge grin of relief. 'You're far too good an actor, Spartacus. For a moment there, I thought I *had* really killed you!'

'You're not nearly as strong as you think, Oenomaus!' said Spartacus, grinning back at the big Gaul. 'My mother used to spank me a lot harder than that when I was a little boy! Come on, we don't have any time to lose.'

They soon had the barrack doors open, releasing the rest of the conspirators – but then things started to go wrong. One of the guards spotted them, and they couldn't stop him from raising the alarm. That brought half a dozen soldiers running, although the legionaries paused when they realised they were outnumbered.

There was no choice for the gladiators but to fight. Spartacus saw a heap of cut wood nearby, logs ready to be burnt in the ovens of the school kitchen. He grabbed one and smashed it over the helmet of the leading soldier, sending him sprawling. Spartacus grabbed the soldier's sword and turned to his friends.

'With me, lads!' he yelled, remembering his father's rallying battle cry, and the gladiators quickly overwhelmed the other soldiers. But everyone else in the school had heard the clamour. Gladiators still in their cells yelled to be let out.

'We can't just leave them behind,' said Oenomaus. 'It wouldn't be fair!'

'Never mind being fair,' muttered Crixus. 'We have to leave now or none of us will escape. The guards are getting organised, and more soldiers are coming!'

'No,' Spartacus said. 'Oenomaus is right. We can't leave them behind.'

He gave the order to release all the gladiators in the school. Then they armed themselves with knives and skewers from the kitchen, and fell on the hated guards and soldiers like hungry wolves. After a brief but brutal fight, every guard and soldier was dead, and the gladiators set fire to some of the buildings. Night had fallen, and red flames leapt into the dark, moonless sky. The gladiators roared in their triumph.

'I was hoping we might be able to get away a little more quietly than this,' groaned Spartacus. 'Everyone for miles around will be able to see that fire.'

'Oh, well, they would have found out sooner or later,' said Crixus. 'What happened to Lentulus, by the way? I was hoping I'd be the one to kill him.'

'He was off down the road like a frightened rabbit,' said Oenomaus. He laughed and slapped Spartacus on the back, almost knocking him over. 'You have led us to a great victory, Spartacus. The question is – what do we do now?'

Oenomaus and Crixus looked at their young friend, and Spartacus took a deep breath. He had been wondering about that himself. There was no chance of lying low in the hills now. But he was their leader, so he was the one who would have to come up with an answer...

5

Into the Volcano

Summer 73BC

Spartacus got the men out of the school as quickly as possible, knowing that more soldiers would be coming. The Gods of all their tribes and countries must have been smiling down on the gladiators, for they had a stroke of luck almost immediately. Not long after sunrise they encountered a couple of wagons on the road – wagons full of new military supplies, swords and spears and armour.

It was all on its way from Rome to the local fort, but Spartacus ordered the wagons to be seized, and soon his men were armed as well as any Roman soldiers. That was very useful, for further down the same road they encountered a column of soldiers who had been sent to catch and kill them. It seemed Lentulus Batiatus had made it to the very same fort and told the commander about the escape.

'What now, Spartacus?' said Oenomaus. 'It looks like we're outnumbered.'

The odds were definitely in favour of the Romans. Spartacus had fewer than a hundred men, and he could see there were at least three times as many soldiers.

'But they haven't realised who we are yet,' said Spartacus, smiling. 'All they can see is a bunch of men wearing Roman armour – so they think we're Roman soldiers, too. We'll wait till they're really close … then we'll let them have it!'

The plan worked brilliantly. At the last moment, Spartacus gave the order, and his men charged into the amazed – and horrified – Roman soldiers. Shortly afterwards, most of the soldiers lay dead on the road, and the survivors were running away as fast as their legs could carry them. The gladiators laughed and jeered, but Spartacus was already thinking about what their next move should be.

'We can't stay on the road,' he said to Crixus

and Oenomaus. 'This is where they'll come looking for us, and next time we'll be even more outnumbered.'

So they headed across country, making for the coast, keeping to hidden tracks through the woods wherever they could. By the time night fell they had arrived at Mount Vesuvius, the great volcano that rose above the Campanian plain. One of the gladiators had grown up in the area, and said that the God of the volcano rumbled and grumbled sometimes, but also that it hadn't erupted for centuries.

Spartacus thought the volcano's crater would be a good place to hide for a few days. A narrow, rocky path led up to a flat area covered with wild vines, and there was plenty of space for a camp. Spartacus sent men out to find food and water – but that turned out to be a mistake. A couple were caught by the Romans, and tortured until they revealed where the main band of runaways could be found.

The next morning, the gladiators woke to find that the path up to the crater – the only way in and out – was blocked by a large force of Romans.

'Well, that's ruined my day, and it's only just started,' said Crixus, peering over the rim of the crater. 'I think the fort must have sent for reinforcements.'

'We've had it!' said Oenomaus. 'There must be five hundred soldiers out there!'

'They could have five *thousand* men and it wouldn't make any difference,' said Spartacus. 'A dozen of us can hold that path and stop them getting in.'

'But we're trapped, Spartacus,' said Crixus. 'How can we get out?'

'Good question, Crixus,' said Spartacus. 'And luckily, I have a pretty good answer.'

Spartacus had been thinking about the wild vines covering the rocky floor of the crater... It had occurred to him that if they plaited them together, they might be strong enough to hold a man's weight. So that day, while some of his men held off the inevitable Roman attempts to break in, the rest cut the vines and made them into ropes.

Night fell, and the Romans stopped attacking, but they left a strong force on the path to make sure the gladiators didn't try to escape. But the narrow entrance to the crater meant that the Romans couldn't see what was going on inside. So they didn't know that later that night the gladiators all quietly climbed down the far side of the crater on their ropes made of vines. Spartacus was the last man to leave. He found his men waiting for him in a hollow at the bottom.

'We could sneak off into the dark now,' he said. 'But I've got a better idea. Let's give the Romans a surprise, and make them think twice about following us.'

The men all murmured their agreement, and Spartacus quickly gave his orders. He divided his small force into two groups, and sent them round either side of the volcano so they could attack the Roman camp from two different directions at the same time. They crept up to the Roman tents, silently cut the throats of the sentries ... then exploded into the camp, yelling their war cries.

For a few moments there was chaos – men running, blades rising and falling, flames leaping into the night sky as tents were set on fire. But it soon became clear that Spartacus had won another victory. Many of the Romans lay dead, and those still alive were running into the darkness, their weapons abandoned.

'I'm beginning to think you're good at this, Spartacus,' said Oenomaus.

'Me, too!' laughed Crixus, wiping the blood from his sword. 'We showed those Romans! Why don't we chase *them* all the way to their fort?'

'Sorry, Crixus, not this time,' said Spartacus. 'We should move on. We don't have a big enough army to take on a whole fort full of Roman soldiers.'

Spartacus was completely right, of course. But things were about to change...

Meanwhile, at a private dinner in Rome, a plump senator was keeping his guest – a fellow senator – entertained with stories of how he had forced a number of peasants to sell him their farms at prices well below their value. Both men lay on couches, and while the plump senator talked, a slave wiped his hands with scented water, careful to clean the heavy gold rings that adorned seven of his ten fingers. The senator shooed the slave away and held up his silver goblet for another slave to refill. Several more slaves continually shuffled in and out of the room, bringing dishes heaped with roast giraffe and elephant, and plates of tiny stuffed quails and mice. A broad silver platter carrying salted snails on a bed of Egyptian lentils was placed at the centre of the table.

'The dancing girls you gave me are incredible, Crassus,' said the plump senator at last, a smile on his face. 'They must have cost an absolute fortune!'

'Think nothing of it, Quintus,' murmured Crassus, a tall, lean man with cold, calculating eyes. It was a warm evening, and four slaves stood behind the two noble Romans, fanning them with huge palm leaves. 'It was the least I could do after your support in the senate against Pompey. I am always very generous to my friends.'

Pompey was another great Roman, a rich man and a soldier, and he and Crassus had long been deadly rivals.

'Yes, well,' said Quintus, shifting uncomfortably under the other man's unrelenting gaze. 'It's, er ... always a pleasure to help you, of course. Still, let's not talk of such serious things. I'm in a mood to see those dancers again!'

Just then another slave entered the room and whispered into his master's ear.

'What a nuisance,' said Quintus, tutting as he waved the slave away. 'It seems some gladiators have escaped from a school near one of my farms.'

'Really?' Crassus remarked, his eyes glittering. 'How interesting...'

6

An Army Gathers

Summer 73BC to spring 72BC

News of the gladiator revolt in Capua spread through the Italian countryside like fire in a field of dry grass after a long, hot summer. Slaves everywhere were thrilled to hear that others like them had escaped and regained their freedom – and had defeated the Roman soldiers sent to re-capture them not just once, but twice.

Soon more and more slaves were running away to join Spartacus. Every day on their way west to the sea, Spartacus and his men found themselves mobbed by crowds of cheering slaves – more gladiators, farm labourers, domestic servants, men, women and children. Spartacus had no choice but to let them join the march.

'What are we going to do with all these people?' said Oenomaus. He and Crixus and Spartacus were standing on a hillside, looking down at the huge crowd. 'They seem to think you can save them from the Romans, Spartacus.'

'We're going to need a lot of ships … if that's still the plan,' said Crixus.

Spartacus didn't reply for a moment, obviously lost in thought. 'No, I've changed my mind,' he said at last. 'We'll never find enough ships for everyone. I think we should keep walking, but head due north instead. You two said your homelands lie beyond the great white mountains, the Alps. I can probably find my way home once we cross them, and so could most of these people, too.'

'But that's impossible!' said Crixus. 'The Romans will never let us march the length of Italy. I know we've beaten them a couple of times, but they'll put out a full army to stop us escaping that way. The legions will cut us to pieces.'

'Are you so sure, Crixus?' said Spartacus. 'What if we gather an army of our own? We've practically got one already. How many people are down there?'

'Ten, maybe twelve thousand,' said Oenomaus. 'And more are still coming in.'

'You see?' said Spartacus, grinning at his friends. 'We can train them – the Romans won't be expecting that, will they? And a true army of slaves will be unbeatable. Every soldier in it has nothing to lose, and loathes the Romans with passion.'

'I don't know if any army is unbeatable,' said Crixus, frowning. 'But there's plenty of gold to grab on the way north. So I'm willing to follow your lead, Spartacus ... for now, that is.'

It was the turn of Oenomaus to raise a bushy eyebrow. Spartacus simply shrugged, however. He had too much on his mind to worry about Crixus...

First Spartacus marched the horde of slaves back towards Vesuvius, and once again set up camp inside its crater. Even though there was the possibility they could be trapped as before, it was still the best place to hide. This time the camp was much bigger, and the people who couldn't fight –

the children and the women and the old – were put to work baking bread and making and mending equipment.

The gladiators taught the men how to fight, but Spartacus had seen the Romans in battle, and he knew that an army should be more than just a collection of warriors. Men are strongest when they work together, so he sought out slaves who were ex-legionaries, deserters from the army who had been captured and sold into slavery as a punishment. With their help, he organised the men into units like those in the Roman army itself – a hundred men to a century, five centuries to a cohort, ten cohorts to a legion. Soon he had the equivalent of two legions, but he kept them training constantly, pushing the men hard, knowing they didn't have much time.

The Romans came for them in the first days of autumn, three full legions tramping up the slopes of Vesuvius. Spartacus stood on the crater rim and watched them, then he ordered his men into position. For many it would be their first battle, and the young Thracian could see the fear in their faces. But he could see hatred there, too, the fury

41

at what Rome had subjected them to.

The battle was long and bloody. The Romans threw their full force at the centre of the slave army, and came close to breaking through. But Spartacus sent Crixus and Oenomaus around the flanks with his best warriors to attack the Romans from behind. Then he gave the order to charge in the centre, leading his men from the front. The slaves pushed forward in their units, remembering their training, each man releasing years of anger with every blow, and eventually the Roman line was smashed.

Only a handful of Romans survived that day.

Spartacus took the defeated legions' equipment and gave it to his men. When a second Roman force attacked a few weeks later, the slaves were more than ready. They had already fought a battle and won. They were confident Spartacus would lead them to another victory, which in due course he did. Now they were a proper army, ready to face whatever stood in their path…

In Rome, the Senate was in total uproar. Gellius

Publicola, the commander of the defeated force, stood before the tiered half-circle of angry senators, all of them demanding to know how he had lost a battle to a mob of slaves. His head was hung low in humiliation and shame. One senator – Crassus – called for order, and eventually walked out in front of the others with his arms raised. The shouting slowly died down.

'My fellow senators,' said Crassus. 'So far we have only sent small forces against these slaves, assuming that a few legions should find it easy to defeat them. This has not been the case.' A murmur of agreement passed through his audience. 'So now the time has come for more serious measures. The rebellion is an affront to the dignity of Rome and we must crush it without mercy. I propose therefore that we put the largest possible force into the field, and that it should be led to victory by none other than this body's noble leaders – our consuls!'

The consuls – Lucullus and Cotta – stood up to accept the honour, and the senate chamber filled with cheering. Two old senators looked on from the back row, both wearing frowns.

'It's not like Crassus to put someone else forward when there's some glory to be had,' one whispered. 'What do you think the crafty devil is up to, Titus?'

'Setting them up for a fall, dear Marcus,' said the other. 'If they succeed, he's the genius who suggested it. But if they fail, he steps in and takes the glory.'

'Ah, yes, of course!' said Marcus. 'We'd better send a message to Spain. I'm sure Pompey will be very interested to know what his rival is up to…'

The army of slaves set off in the spring, heading north as Spartacus had planned, using the long, straight roads the Romans were so proud of to escape. Spartacus had made sure his army was well supplied with food and weapons, and he insisted that good order was kept on the march.

But they soon encountered opposition. Like any skilful general, Spartacus sent out scouts ahead, and one came riding back with bad news.

'It's the Romans!' the man yelled in panic. 'There are thousands of them!'

Spartacus went forward with Crixus and Oenomaus to see for himself. The scout was right – at least four full legions of the Roman army stood facing them a mile or so up the road. Bright sunlight glittered on Roman helmets and shields and spear points … and suddenly Spartacus remembered standing on a hillside in Thrace. This time he was determined things would be different.

In any case, he could see that the Roman generals had picked a bad spot to fight a battle. Their legions were lined up across the floor of a valley, with nothing but low hills on either side. So it should be easy to send some of his men round behind them with Crixus and Oenomaus, as he had done before…

The battle was short and savage. The Romans never expected to be attacked from the front and the rear. Hundreds of legionaries were cut down before their commanders realised what had happened. Spears flew through the air, blades crashed on shields or on other blades, blood flowed, men sweated and grunted and screamed and died. Spartacus looked on, hating the waste of life. But he hated his enemy more, so he smiled

45

when the legions suddenly broke and ran, leaving the slave army to cheer its greatest victory, and the general they loved.

It was a good moment, one he would remember in the dark times ahead.

7
Parting of the Ways

Summer to autumn 72BC

That night, the slave army celebrated. People from all the nations the Romans had conquered danced round their campfires, and sang and drank the wine they had looted from Roman towns and villas. Spartacus laughed and danced, too, happy for the first time in many years.

He could hardly believe what his raggle-taggle army of runaway slaves had just achieved. After the battle, he had discovered that they had defeated a force commanded by the consuls, the two most powerful leaders of the Roman state. They had captured the sacred Eagle standards of a couple of the legions as well. Every Roman soldier was supposed to lay down his life rather than surrender any of the Eagles, so it was a huge blow to the prestige of the Roman army.

After a while, Spartacus grew tired and went to his tent. He wanted to get some sleep, knowing there would be a lot to do in the morning. The road to the white mountains lay before them, and the Romans still had plenty of legions left...

Suddenly the tent flap flew open and Oenomaus strode in, his face grim.

'Come with me, Spartacus,' he said. 'There's something you should see.'

Spartacus was puzzled, and followed the big Gaul out. They hurried through the camp, most of which seemed strangely empty and quiet now. Then Spartacus began to hear what sounded like a big crowd yelling and cheering. Eventually, he and Oenomaus came to a place where a large circle had been marked with flaming torches stuck in the ground. The crowd making all the noise were standing around the circle, their attention fixed on what was happening inside it.

Two men were fighting, one armed with a sword and shield, the other with a spear. Spartacus saw immediately that they were captured Roman soldiers, and that they clearly didn't want to fight. But every time they lowered their weapons or begged for mercy, they were threatened by the crowd. There were more soldiers waiting at the edge of the circle, a whole line of them with their hands tied.

'Welcome to our little entertainment, Spartacus!' yelled a familiar voice. Spartacus looked up and saw Crixus sitting on a wagon beyond the circle. The wagon was stacked with Roman weapons and furniture and chests full of coins and jewels, and Crixus was grinning happily. 'At last, it's us slaves making the Romans fight for *our* pleasure!' he laughed. 'Now that's what I call justice!'

A roar of approval went up from the crowd, and the Romans in the circle fell to their knees, terrified. Spartacus glanced at Oenomaus, then stepped forward into the torchlight and strode over to Crixus. The German's smile quickly faded.

'This isn't justice, Crixus,' said Spartacus. 'I hate the Romans more than anybody, but you're making us the same as them... It's wrong to force men to fight each other.'

'Well, I don't agree,' muttered Crixus, scowling. 'And I'm not the only one who feels that way. The Romans treat their animals better than they treated us.'

'Maybe so,' growled Spartacus. 'But we're not Romans. I am your leader, and my orders are that this is to stop. Does everybody understand?'

He looked round the circle of faces in the flickering torchlight, many of them sullen. There were a few murmurs, but Spartacus knew he had won. He gave orders for the Roman prisoners to be released at some distance from the camp – it seemed the safest thing to do – then returned to his tent. He slept badly, a nightmare taking him back to the arena, the dead Retiarius standing over him…

There were more arguments with Crixus over the following weeks. Spartacus had given orders that loot should be shared equally between everyone in the army, but Crixus refused to hand his over. Spartacus told the army to get ready to march north, but Crixus wasn't sure that was such a good idea any more.

'I don't particularly want to live in a damp

German forest,' he said. 'Not when Italy is wide open to us. Think of the loot, Spartacus! It's ours for the taking. We could be richer than the richest Romans. We could live like kings!'

Spartacus listened ... then told Crixus that the army would be heading north, as they had planned. Crixus glared at him, then stomped off to his tent.

Two mornings later, Crixus rode out of the camp at the head of at least one third of the army, all those who agreed with him that gathering loot was more important than going home.

Spartacus watched them leave, with Oenomaus beside him.

'The parting of the ways,' said Oenomaus. 'So much for being brothers.'

'They will always be our brothers,' said Spartacus. Then he turned on his heel and walked away. 'Come, Oenomaus. We must prepare for our march.'

The Senate had been in session for hours. They had interrogated Lucullus and Cotta and a vote had exiled both consuls as a punishment for their disgrace.

After they left the chamber, Quintus, the plump senator, heaved himself up from his seat next to Crassus and nervously addressed his peers. He waved his hands through the air as he spoke, and everyone's eyes were drawn to the heavy gold rings adorning seven of his ten fingers. Crassus simply stared into the distance.

'Noble Senators of Rome,' said Quintus. 'Rarely in our history have we been faced with such terrible danger. This army of slaves has defeated everything we have sent against them. More slaves are escaping every day, and the forces of this Spartacus grow like a deadly sickness in our great fatherland. I therefore propose that the most severe punishments be given to any runaways who are caught!'

'Seconded,' cried a voice from the back, and other senators yelled their agreement.

'Good, good,' said Quintus, holding up his hand for silence. 'And now to the matter of dealing with the slave army itself. I put it to you that we still have plenty of reserve legions, but there is only one man who can save us! He alone has the resources, the strength and the strategic genius to lead us to victory...'

'I'll bet ten gold pieces he's not talking about you, Marcus,' Titus whispered to his friend. The two old senators were sitting in their usual places at the back.

'That's a wager I won't take,' replied Marcus. 'I know where this is going.'

Quintus had paused for effect. At last he cried out, 'That man is Crassus!' and the Senate roared its approval. Titus and Marcus frowned at each other.

Crassus rose from his seat and walked out to stand before the Senate. 'I swear that I will fulfil the task given to me by you, the greatest, most noble assembly in the world!' he said, his voice ringing out loud and clear in the chamber. 'I will bring you victory, and recover our sacred Eagles! And in doing so I will send a message to every slave – great Rome is your master, now and for all eternity!'

'Rousing stuff,' said Titus as cheering broke out and senators crowded round Crassus. 'You have to hand it to him – the man plays a very shrewd game.'

'Indeed he does,' said Marcus. 'I think it's time for another letter to Pompey…'

On the third day after Crixus left, the slave army arrived at the main pass through the Alps. Only a small force of Romans – a single cohort – barred their way. Spartacus sent an envoy to the legionaries, offering them the chance to retreat. He didn't want to see anybody else die, not when the slaves were so close to going home. The reply was a single spear thrown at the messenger.

It was a brutal fight, and a fast one, too. The Romans never stood a chance, the slaves attacking from all sides at once. They knew that this was the last obstacle on their long journey, and they quickly overwhelmed the legionaries.

After the battle, a lone rider appeared from the south. 'You must come at once, Spartacus,' he said, reining in his tired horse. 'Crixus is surrounded!'

Spartacus looked at the entrance to the pass for a moment, but he knew he couldn't desert his friend. Soon they were marching southwards once more…

8

Relentless Pursuit

Late autumn 72BC

They were a day late. Spartacus and his army arrived to find a scene of utter carnage. Crixus had been defeated, and his men left to rot on the battlefield – those that had been lucky enough to die there. Anyone captured alive had been tortured, then strung up on trees. Spartacus could imagine the Romans jeering as his friends had slowly bled to death. Not a single runaway slave had survived.

Spartacus gave orders for Crixus to be buried where he had died, in the thick of the fighting, and for the other bodies to be burned. The flames roared for three days, and thick black smoke filled the sky. For most of the time Spartacus sat on a hill nearby, watching and brooding, refusing to speak to anybody.

It was Oenomaus who finally got through to him. 'People keep asking what we're going to do now, Spartacus,' the Gaul said gently. 'I don't think we can stay here much longer. The scouts tell me the Romans are coming back, maybe with six legions. And there aren't quite as many of us as there were before…'

'Don't you think I know that?' Spartacus snapped. But then he sighed. 'I'm sorry, Oenomaus,' he said. 'I shouldn't take it out on you. You're right, of course. We need to be moving. Six legions, you say? How close are they?'

'No more than half a day's march at the most,' said Oenomaus. 'So, what's the plan now? We'll have to get a move on if we're going to try the Alps again. It will take us six or seven days to get back there, and it won't be long before the winter snow starts to block the high passes.'

'That occurred to me, too,' said Spartacus. 'We don't have any choice but to head back to the coast again. It looks like we'll have to escape by sea after all. I've been thinking about where we

can find enough boats for everybody, and I have an idea.'

A while ago, Spartacus had heard some of his men talking about pirates, and he remembered the legionary on the ship bringing him to Rome had talked about them as well. He interrogated his men, and soon discovered that the seas around Italy were full of pirate ships. The slave army had plenty of treasure, and Spartacus wondered if they could use it to buy their way to freedom.

It was worth a try, so Spartacus marched his army south, searching for an isolated part of the west coast where he could make contact with the pirates. Day after day, the slaves trudged down long, straight roads, the six legions pursuing them, but never attacking, or even getting any closer.

'This is even worse than waiting to go into the arena,' Oenomaus muttered at last. 'I wish they'd catch up with us ... then we could have a proper battle.'

'Why should they?' said Spartacus. 'They can afford to play a waiting game. We're losing people, and the Romans have made sure we won't get any more.'

Spartacus had found out that most slaves were far too scared to run away from their masters now. Any slaves caught trying to escape were killed, usually as painfully as possible. And many of those who had joined Spartacus were leaving, convinced the Romans would win in the end. As they marched, the deserters slipped into the hills or woods, or even the cities where it was easy to hide in the crowded slums.

'Maybe we should just attack Rome and be done with it,' said Oenomaus. 'Kill the rich Romans, burn the Senate, bring down the whole rotten lot.'

'What then, Oenomaus?' said Spartacus. 'Either they'd wait for us to leave and simply start again, or we'd have to run things ourselves. And before you knew it, *we'd* be the ones conquering foreign lands and selling their peoples into slavery. No, I don't want anything to do with the city of Rome.'

'Well, when you put it like that...' said Oenomaus, laughing. 'But I'd still like to cut the throats of a few more Romans before we go sailing with the pirates.'

Oenomaus got his wish a few days later. The scouts told Spartacus that the Romans had split their force in two. The Thracian realised immediately it was part of a plan to surround his army, and perhaps even spring a trap on them. So he sprang a trap on them instead, marching through the night with his best troops and striking the three nearest legions hard and fast. It was another victory for Spartacus, and the sight of Roman soldiers fleeing from his slave army made him laugh with joy.

But it didn't stop the pursuit. The Roman legions kept following, and sometimes Spartacus could even hear the *tramp-tramp-tramp* of their feet in his dreams...

Crassus ordered the survivors of the three defeated legions to assemble in front of him in their camp. He stood on a raised platform with his officers and stared silently down at the nervous legionaries, his cold, hard eyes raking over them.

At last, he spoke. 'You have brought shame to your Eagles,' he said, his voice cutting through them like a knife. 'You broke and ran, and Rome will not stand for cowardice in its soldiers. I therefore have one word for you – *Decimation*.'

LIVESinACTION

It was an ancient and terrible punishment. Under the steely gaze of Crassus, each legionary stepped forward to draw a pebble from a great urn, its narrow neck making it impossible to see what was inside. Nine out of every ten pebbles were white, but the tenth was black. The first soldier to pick a black pebble dropped it, his hands shaking, and the legionaries behind him stepped back, as if they were scared they might be infected by his bad luck. But soon other soldiers formed a tight circle round the doomed man, and all that could be seen were their wooden clubs rising and falling as they beat him to death. Every tenth man in the defeated legions died that day, and the killing went on for hours.

'Well, I think I made my point,' Crassus said to the young officer beside him when it was finished, and the cowed legions marched away to their barracks.

'Yes, commander,' murmured the officer, barely able to look him in the eye.

'Do show some backbone, Marcellus,' snapped Crassus. 'Never forget that these soldiers are barely human, little different to the slaves we are hunting.

Italy is full of the kind of scum only too happy to swell the ranks of the legions, but we have to rule them with an iron rod, or they will rise up against us, too…'

Spartacus was in his tent, studying a Roman army map of Italy laid out on a table, both items looted from a Roman fort. It was late autumn, and they had finally managed to reach the coast in the far south of the Italian peninsula.

'How strange…' said Oenomaus. 'It's shaped like a foot – there's the heel!'

'And we're right at the end of the toe,' murmured Spartacus, deep in thought. 'That's probably not such a good place to be with a large Roman army behind us. If we can't escape from here by sea, we might end up completely trapped.'

A couple of days later the Romans started building a wall to seal them in.

9
Besieged

The legions were good at building fortifications –
it was something Roman soldiers were trained to
do. Soon a wall of rough logs stretched from coast
to coast, right across the 'toe' of Italy, bottling up
Spartacus and his whole army. The wall was taller
than two men, had watch towers every few miles
and a ditch in front of it filled with sharpened
stakes and nettles. But there were no gates.

'It must have a weakness somewhere,' said
Spartacus. He and Oenomaus were hiding inside
an ancient olive grove that stood on a slope near
the wall. They had crept as close as they could to
examine the barrier that penned them in like cattle

or sheep. 'We'll just have to keep probing till we find it, that's all.'

Spartacus had ordered attacks on the wall throughout the winter, but none so far had been successful. Spring was coming and he had heard that yet another Roman army was on its way. This one had arrived in the north of Italy from Spain and was under the command of Pompey, a powerful rival to Crassus. Spartacus had a feeling that Crassus wasn't the type to share a victory, and would be increasingly desperate to finish things off.

'It won't matter, though,' said Oenomaus, grinning. 'Not once you've struck your deal with the pirates, anyway. Then we can kiss goodbye to Crassus.'

'That might not be quite as easy as we'd been hoping,' said Spartacus. 'In fact, I'm beginning to think that we might have to forget the whole idea…'

It had taken a while to make contact with any pirates, and striking a deal had turned out to be very difficult. There was no overall pirate leader, and none of the individual pirate chiefs had enough ships to take the whole slave army. Spartacus didn't trust them, either. They wanted to be paid first, and Spartacus thought they might simply take the money and run without fulfilling their part of the bargain. Or make even more money by selling the slave army back to the Romans.

'So that's it, then,' muttered Oenomaus. 'We can't hold out here for ever – we'll starve long before the end of the year. We're short of food already.'

'Well, I'm not giving up yet,' said Spartacus. 'We might not be able to find enough pirate ships for us all to escape. But we can certainly buy a few. And we could use them to get a small force round behind the wall. Then we can attack in one sector and control it long enough to let the rest of the army through.'

'I like it!' said Oenomaus, his grin restored. 'You really *are* a genius!'

Several days later, on a dark, moonless night, three ships sailed silently into a bay on the coast just behind the Roman wall and ran right up onto the beach. A group of men – the last of the original gladiators and the best of the others in the slave army, led by Spartacus himself – jumped onto the sand and moved like ghosts towards the nearby Roman camp, swords and spears at the ready. Within minutes, the camp had been overrun and the slaves set to work on the wall…

By the time the sun rose, a large section of the Roman wall had been broken down, and the main body of the slave army was marching north again.

'We did it, Spartacus!' said Oenomaus. 'Nothing can stop us now!'

Spartacus didn't say a word. He only hoped Oenomaus was right…

'Pompey is *where*?' Crassus roared.

He was leaning over the map table in the sumptuous tent at the heart of his army's camp, his officers bustling around him. A messenger had just arrived, and the news the young cavalryman had brought was obviously unwelcome.

'Sir, he is fifty miles north of Rome,' the messenger murmured, swallowing hard. 'He has let it be known that he is hurrying to bring you reinforcements.'

'Has he now?' Crassus said coldly. 'The truth is

he's come to steal my glory. Well, I won't let the swine get away with it.' He turned to his officers. 'Draw up plans for an immediate sweep from the wall to the sea. I want the slaves wiped out and Spartacus captured long before Pompey reaches us.'

His officers started pulling more maps from chests and spread them on the table. Suddenly, a centurion walked in and stood to attention before Crassus.

'Sir, there are disturbing reports from the northern sector,' he said. 'It seems that the slaves seized part of the wall during the night and, er … have broken out!'

Crassus stared at the centurion for the space of five heartbeats. Then he strapped on his sword-belt with great deliberation and strode from the tent, his long red cloak swirling, his officers and the centurion following in his wake.

The young cavalryman stood alone in the empty tent, and realised he had been holding his breath. He let it out, then ran to catch up with the others.

By early spring, Spartacus had led his army halfway up the Italian peninsula.

'We'll stop here, Oenomaus,' he said one day. They had arrived at the coast again, but this time in the east, on the Adriatic. Spartacus knew that beyond the sparkling blue sea lay Greece and the Balkans, and his homeland, Thrace...

'Are you sure, Spartacus?' said Oenomaus. 'Crassus isn't far behind us. He could be marching over those hills tomorrow, and then we'll have to fight.'

'We don't really have much choice, old friend,' said Spartacus. 'Pompey isn't that far away, either. The last thing we want is for him to join forces with Crassus.'

'They hate each other too much to do that, don't they?' said Oenomaus.

'They hate us more,' said Spartacus. 'And we can't take the risk. It's better for us to fight them one at a time. We'll have more of a chance that way.'

'I'll take your word for it,' said Oenomaus, smiling at his friend.

'I'd better be right then,' said Spartacus,

smiling, too. He looked round at the low hills and his army. A breath of wind whispered off the waves, carrying with it the smell of salt. 'This is as good a place for a battle as any,' he said.

It might even be a good place to die, he thought. But he didn't say it.

10

The Last Battle

Summer 71 BC

Spartacus stood on the hillside in the centre of his army, watching the Romans marching towards them. Italian sunlight glinted off the Roman helmets and spears and shields, and the ground shook beneath the *tramp-tramp-tramping* of Roman feet. Memories flooded through him once again at the sight of their red crests.

'Steady, lads,' said Spartacus. He wondered if he sounded like his father.

He looked at the people around him, the slaves who had flocked to join his great rebellion against Rome. And just as on that fateful morning in Thrace, they were young and old and every age in between. Nobody there was related to him, but he thought of them as family. They were all his brothers and sisters.

'That's quite some army Crassus has,' said Oenomaus, shielding his eyes from the sun with his hand. 'I'd say we've definitely got him worried.'

Spartacus laughed. 'Well, it's about time the Romans started taking us seriously,' he said. 'They'll know they've been in a battle, anyway.'

He glimpsed a tall figure riding a white horse behind the advancing lines of Roman soldiers, and realised it must be Crassus himself. The Roman general's red crest was the tallest of all, and his armour shone with a dazzling glow.

'Right, it looks like things are about to get started,' murmured Oenomaus.

Spartacus could see that the Romans had halted at last and formed their wall of shields. Soon they would launch their spears into the air, and after that the Gods would decide who might live and who might die. But Spartacus had a few words to say first. He strode out in front of his army and turned to face them.

'I'm not a great believer in speeches,' he yelled,

his voice echoing off the hills. 'But I'll tell you this. I was a slave for only a short while, but I soon found out that anything is better than being a slave of the Romans, and it's for that reason I fought them. Whatever happens, I promised myself I would die a free man. Are you with me in this? Shall we stand together and fight? Shall we fight for freedom?'

'We're all with you, Spartacus!' the whole army roared. 'For freedom!'

Spartacus nodded and raised his sword, then swept it round to point at his hated enemy. 'With me, lads … *NOW!*' he screamed, and he charged down the hillside towards the Roman shields, his army right behind him, whooping their war cries, their feet thundering on the dry ground.

Roman spears flew into the massed ranks of ex-slaves and men fell, screaming in agony. The two armies came together with a CRASH! and the clamour of sword on shield filled the air. Legionaries and ex-slaves alike cried out as sharp metal sliced into soft flesh.

The Romans held their ground, and gradually began to push back their opponents. They outnumbered the slave army by three to one, which meant they could send reserves to any part of their line that might be struggling. The slaves were tired too, from their long journeys up and down Italy, and it wasn't long before Spartacus realised the battle was lost, his army surrounded. They were being slaughtered, and every time Spartacus looked up from the carnage, he saw Crassus on his white horse, calmly giving orders, directing his men.

Oenomaus fought like a hero from some ancient Gaulish tale, but Spartacus saw his friend chopped down at last by three Romans. Spartacus screamed his war cry and hacked through the enemy in front of him, his eyes on Crassus…

The young Thracian came close, although he never really stood a chance. The Roman general's bodyguards formed a ring of steel around him that even Spartacus couldn't get through. He managed to kill two of them, but then a third knocked him down with his shield, and several more slashed at him with their swords. The battle moved on, leaving Spartacus under a heap of bodies, blood flowing from a dozen wounds, any one of which would have killed a lesser man.

As he lay there, the clamour around him seemed to fade, as his mind travelled to a distant place and time. Perhaps he dreamed of his homeland, of a village in the mountains where his family was still alive and waiting for him, his father smiling, standing at the door of his great hall, waiting for his young son to return…

Crassus sat on his white horse, his officers behind him on their mounts. They were watching legionaries nailing the survivors of the slave army to tall wooden crosses along the Appian Way, the high road to Rome. For this was crucifixion, another ancient and terrible punishment, an agonising ordeal that sometimes took days to kill a man. Yet Crassus smiled coldly as the victims screamed, and those waiting to be crucified sobbed and begged their captors for mercy.

'Come, gentlemen,' Crassus said eventually, wheeling his horse round and trotting away. 'I must be in Rome before Pompey gets there and speaks to the Senate. I wouldn't put it past the old devil to try and steal my glory.'

'Oh, I hardly think he'll be able to, sir,' Marcellus said eagerly, riding a little behind his commander. 'But I've been wondering – do you think we'll have any more trouble with slaves? Or that another Spartacus might appear?'

'No on both counts, Marcellus,' said Crassus as they passed the gate of a farm on one side of the road. He laughed and nodded at the two lines of crosses stretching into the far distance. 'This is a lesson even a slave can learn.'

A slave was standing at the gate, and heard what Crassus said. He watched the rich, powerful Romans ride on, waiting until they had gone.

Then the slave turned so he couldn't be seen, and spat into the Roman dust.

THE
ROAD TO
WAR

ALPS

Crixus's
last battle

Adriatic Sea

Rome

Capua

Mount
Vesuvius

Mediterranean
Sea

Site of
last battle

Line of
Roman
defences

Index